The Legend of Kitch-iti-kipi

Carole Lynn Hare
(Miskwa Anang Kwe)

Illustrations and cover design by Ryan Gilroy, Manistique, MI

Poor Richards Castle books may be ordered through booksellers
or by contacting:

Richards Printing
718 Ludington Street
Escanaba, Michigan 49829
P: (906) 786-3540 • F: (906) 786-6068
E: office@richardsprinting.net

ISBN: 978-0-578-78251-5

Printed in the United States of America

I dedicate this book to my father, Jerome.
His many years of diligent research, hard work,
and leadership helped create the strong tribal organization
and benefits we all enjoy today.

Because of him, I am a proud member of the Sault Ste. Marie
Tribe of Chippewa Indians and have this story to tell.

Jerome Peterson

What Is Kitch-iti-kipi?

KITCH-ITI-KIPI is a natural wonder and tourist attraction located about twelve miles outside of Manistique, Michigan, near Indian Lake in the Upper Peninsula. It is Michigan's largest freshwater spring. In the Ojibwe language, the name means "Big Spring." It has also been called "Mirror of Heaven."

Many tourists come to see this giant pond measuring 300 by 175 feet, and 42 feet deep. Over 10,000 gallons of water per minute gush up through the cracks in the bottom rock, creating many small pockets of swirling sand. Because it is spring-fed, the water temperature is a constant 45 degrees year-round and remains crystal clear. The pond is filled with huge fallen trees and gigantic trout, which can be seen through the glass bottom windows of the self-operated raft used by visitors.

In the 1920s, John I. Bellair, owner of the dime store in Manistique, discovered and fell in love with this beautiful water hole hidden in the deep woods near Indian Lake. Bellair used to take groups of people across the Big Spring himself in his own boat, but in 1926, he persuaded the owner of the land, Palms Book Land Company, to sell the spring and surrounding 90 acres to the state of Michigan for $10. The sale stipulated that the property was "to be forever used as a public park, bearing the name Palms Book State Park."

Several different legends exist about Kitch-iti-kipi; many were thought to have been made up by John Bellair himself to entice tourists to visit the area. Mr. Bellair actually admitted this later in his life. The legend I share in this book is one passed down through many generations in my Native American family, long before John Bellair discovered Kitch-iti-kipi.[1]

---

[1] Information for this introduction comes from these articles:
"KITCH-ITI-KIPI." Manistique Tourism Council.
https://www.visitmanistique.com/bigspring.shtml
"Kitch-iti-kipi – Palms Book State Park." Visit Escanaba, Michigan.
https://www.visitescanaba.com/member-detail/kitch-iti-kipi-palms-book-state-park/

Preface

My Native American name is Miskwa Anang Kwe (Red Star Woman), the name given to me by our tribe's traditional healer. I am a member of the Sault Ste. Marie Tribe of Chippewa Indians (sometimes referred to as the Ojibwe or just the Sault Tribe). My father, now ninety-one years old, was born in Thompson, Michigan. Today, he is a highly recognized tribal elder. In 2016, he was presented with an eagle feather (an honor given only to those held in highest esteem) for his many years of service as one of the original organizers of the Sault Tribe. He has led and served on many tribal boards and committees over the years and was instrumental in winning the legal battle for tribal fishing rights in Michigan. Even now, as one of the few elders in their nineties, he is still active, attending local powwows, elder luncheons, and other meetings and activities. His mother, my paternal grandmother, portrayed the true spirit of a Native American woman—gentle, wise, and strong. Her ancestors were the original natives in this area of the Upper Peninsula.

Growing up, I heard the story of Kitch-iti-kipi from several relatives and family friends. Native Americans are notorious for passing on their folklore and colorful legends orally but seldom in writing. My Great-Great-Aunt Pearl, my great-grandma's sister—we just called her Aunt Pearl—was a woman way ahead of her time. She was a well-read, self-educated, and musically talented woman. A hard-working farm wife and mother, she was also politically active. She often expressed her political views to local authorities and to many high-ranking state officials both verbally and in writing.

Aunt Pearl wrote down the legend of Kitch-iti-kipi in a booklet, which was published in 1963 by the local newspaper office here in Manistique, Michigan. Several copies of that booklet were given to my father upon her passing. They had been stored in a box in her old barn on the Thompson farm for many years and were faded and musty. Her account of the legend was similar to what I remember hearing from other relatives growing up, with a few slight variations. I did not know, however, how this story first came to be known in my family until I read Aunt Pearl's booklet.

According to Aunt Pearl, one very cold night in mid-February, her grandma (my great-great-great-grandma) was sitting looking out the window of her cabin in Thompson, Michigan, mesmerized by the falling snow. She noticed something large and dark lying in the snowbank on the road in front of her cabin. She bundled up and went out to find Squaw Mary,[2] an old Indian woman, unconscious and barely breathing.

Squaw Mary had lived in the Thompson area as far back as anyone could remember. When asked, she told people she was more than 100 years old and her ancestors had been the first settlers of Indian Lake. No one knew her full name since she was always only called "Squaw Mary."

Grandma dragged the nearly frozen body of Squaw Mary into the house and put her to bed near the old wood stove. She covered her with heavy wool blankets and prayed over her, asking God to save her life. Later the next day, Squaw Mary finally woke up and Grandma fed her hot soup and homemade bread and gave her special tea to drink. After a couple of days in Grandma's care, Squaw Mary regained her strength and Grandma sent her on her way with a meal and kind words.

---

[2] Today the term "squaw" is considered a derogatory racial slur and extremely insulting to Native American women, who refer to it as the "S" word. Several Native American historians believe the term merely meant an Indian woman or wife. I tell this story as it was told to me using the name, "Squaw Mary"; however, the word squaw should never be used today in reference to a Native American female.

Grandma's kindness was never forgotten by Squaw Mary, and she began to visit Grandma regularly, always bringing her small gifts, as is the Indian way to show gratitude. She called Grandma her "Winter Angel."

On one particular visit, Squaw Mary brought Grandma a huge basket of freshly picked, wild blueberries that grew abundantly in the Thompson woods. While they sat and visited, munching on the sweet berries, Grandma's youngest teenage son came in and said he was going swimming with his friends at Indian Lake.

Squaw Mary became extremely agitated and noticeably upset. She frantically insisted that the young man should not go swimming in Indian Lake or go anywhere near the Big Spring. After much soothing and coaxing, she finally calmed down and explained her reasons for the warning. The story Squaw Mary told my great-great-great-grandma that day is what has been told for more than a hundred years in my family. This, I believe, is the authentic Native American legend of Kitch-iti-kipi.

The Legend of Kitch-iti-kipi

Several hundred years ago, a small tribe of Ojibwe Indians was settling back into their summer territory surrounding the glassy, calm waters of Indian Lake. It had been a long hard journey the previous weeks traveling on foot from their winter settlement far south of the Great Water. The trail they had kept well-marked every year was rugged and they carried heavy loads of all their belongings. The small tribe always returned in the melting season back to the tranquility of this pristine lake hidden in the forests not far from the "Great Water" now known as Lake Michigan.

Robin peeked her head out of her teepee and heard the twittering of the many birds in the trees above her. The pure crisp air filled her lungs and she admired the wet dew dripping on the grass blades as she looked out toward the lake. This place always felt more like home to Robin than any other lands her tribe had settled in and she welcomed being back. It was here that most of the babies of the tribe were born after the long hard winter months had lifted. She once again felt needed and important since she would soon be practicing her honed craft of midwifery again.

In the Ojibwe tribe, the midwife was considered a wise woman and not only seen as a deliverer of babies. The actual term "midwife" among many North American tribes translates to "the one who does everything." She actually had several roles: teacher, healer, caregiver, nurturer, dietician, and deliverer. Her most important title though was "do-dis-seem," which means the spiritual nurturer of the child throughout their life. Robin was the do-dis-seem of many young children growing up in the tribe, and she took her role very seriously. The babies she delivered were like her own children, and she maintained a close relationship with all of them even into adulthood.

As Robin exited her tepee and stood in the morning silence, she began her ritual to prepare herself for the day. She raised her hands high, thanking the Great Spirit for a restful sleep. She then walked quietly down to the water's edge where she knelt and touched the sand. Her prayers were always the same...thankfulness first, then clearing her mind totally and just sitting and listening for whatever Great Spirit would tell her. Her mind was quiet as she waited in silence.

She was as still as a statue for quite some time and finally opened her eyes slowly. The first thing she saw was a young eagle standing at the water's edge gazing out as the gentle waves were lapping at its feet. *Such a beautiful sight!* Robin thought.

Native Americans consider the bald eagle to be a sacred bird because eagles are the highest flying of all birds and, therefore, thought to be closest to God. The eagle represents courage, wisdom, and strength, and its role is to be the communicator with the Creator. Robin watched as the young eagle proudly lifted its wings and took flight over the calm water, which mirrored its beauty and gracefulness.

Robin suddenly knew what Great Spirit was telling her. She had been waiting to be given the name for the child she would deliver later that day or the next. A young girl, Moonbeam, was very near her birthing time and would be the first of many to deliver new babies that spring. Robin was responsible for naming each child she delivered, and she was always given a clear sign of the name to be given. This morning was no exception!

Moonbeam's child would be called Young Eagle. She knew it would be a boy! No one understood how Robin knew these things, but she was never wrong about the sex of the newborns she delivered, and the names given always seemed to suit the child perfectly throughout their life. Robin sensed that just as that young eagle would grow to be outstanding in all ways among his bird species, this first spring baby would grow to be outstanding among the men of the tribe.

With excitement and focus, Robin began her chores of preparing for the birth. She collected fresh lake water in buckets to be heated over the open campfire, which she knew Brave Bear, Moonbeam's husband, would soon have ready. She gathered clean cloths and freshly washed blankets to wrap the newborn in. She grabbed her supplies and walked eagerly to Moonbeam's teepee and shooed the anxious father away. Men were not allowed near the birthing scene until mother and child were bonding comfortably and nursing had begun.

Robin heated the buckets of water near the fire and entered the tent to find Moonbeam lying on her side, moaning in pain. The time was near! Robin calmed Moonbeam with soothing words and stroked her head and back, reminding her of all she had taught her about the birthing process. Moonbeam began to relax, and with each growing pain, Robin assured her all was well. Robin told her of the young eagle and explained that soon she would deliver a healthy baby boy who would be called "Young Eagle." He would stand out among the braves of the tribe. Moonbeam's labor went quickly, and she delivered a strong crying baby boy! Robin wrapped Young Eagle in the fresh blankets and placed him in the arms of his eager mother. Moonbeam gazed into the eyes of her son and felt a love she had never known.

As Young Eagle looked up at his mother with a deep loving gaze, she swore her son was smiling at her. He had a full head of jet-black hair and the most beautiful deep brown eyes! His body was tiny, yet she felt his strength and confidence. The two women were amazed at how Young Eagle latched on for his first meal. Robin laughed and said, "I should have named him Hungry Trout!"

Young Eagle was a healthy baby and was soon known among the other mothers as the happiest, most playful baby among the group of newborns that spring. As a toddler, he won the hearts of all who met him. He had a sweet, loving face with a bright, warm smile that he shared easily with anyone he saw. As he grew older, his features and personality grew even more pleasing. He was loved and admired for both his attractive appearance and his happy, gentle, and kind nature.

Near the end of Young Eagle's second year, the tribe was once again returning to their summer home along the northern shores of Indian Lake. As they approached their destination, they decided to camp overnight near Kitch-iti-kipi (Big Spring) on the south side of the lake. A huge black storm cloud hung very low in the sky, and loud threatening claps of thunder were bursting continuously. They would have to stop for the night and continue to the northern side in the morning after the storm passed.

The teepees were set up just in time. As the storm was about to break into its worst fury, Robin came out from her teepee, once again in quest of a name, this time for the daughter of Little Beaver and Blue Bird, which Blue Bird was very soon going to deliver, most likely that night.

Robin knew she could not go all the way down to the water since the storm was too close, so she stood quietly in a clearing near the forest's edge. She looked down toward the spring and noticed something moving. Slowly stepping into the clearing was a very young fawn approaching the spring. It moved cautiously and deliberately and dipped its nose into the refreshing cool water.

Without making a sound, the fawn bent down gracefully and drank its fill. Then, like a shadow, the fawn slowly disappeared into the darkness of the woods. Robin chuckled as she always did when she was amused by something. She made her way to the tent of Bluebird, who was quickly progressing in labor and told her she would have a daughter who would be named "Little Fawn."

The storm erupted in full force with loud roars like an angry giant! The ferocious wind and beating rain continued throughout the night as Bluebird and Robin concentrated on the birth of Little Fawn. They heard the crashing of trees and felt the ground shake. Finally, as the last hard contraction came and the baby was born, the storm abruptly ended. Not a sound could be heard! It was as if Mother Earth had decided to hold her breath for this child to be born in total peace.

The baby girl was indeed beautiful, and she curled up in her mother's arms nursing calmly and gracefully. Her name, Little Fawn, suited her perfectly! It was hard to believe that throughout the delivery a loud thunderous storm had pounded down around them. The child showed no distress, only quiet contentment.

At daybreak, Robin stepped out onto the wet grass and took note of the storm's aftermath. As she walked toward the spring, everywhere she saw huge trees torn up by their roots lying like fallen warriors. When she reached the water's edge, she noticed many of the giant trees had fallen into the clear deep water and the underground spring bubbled up around them. Such a beautiful peaceful sight after the raging storm the previous night.

Two days later, after Robin had collected her own belongings, she helped Bluebird bundle up Little Fawn to carry her in the new cradleboard made by the older ladies of the village. It was time for the tribe to move to the northern side of Indian Lake and settle for the summer and fall.

As they worked, Robin noticed Big Buck, the twelve-year-old son of Chief Eagle Feather, watching them. Big Buck was a mean, cantankerous little boy. His eyes were close together, small and beady. He had a pointy nose set between his eyes that looked like the beak of a hawk. His cheekbones were so high that his face looked out of proportion with his straight black hair, which always hung over his forehead, accentuating his evil-looking eyes. He was a short, muscular boy and had the strength of a full-grown man. Big Buck was a bully who played mean tricks on the other children, so they avoided him.

In contrast, Young Eagle had many friends, young and old, because of his kind and friendly personality.

Young Eagle and Little Fawn were playmates and grew to be inseparable throughout their childhood and teen years. Young Eagle was favored by the elders and taught many skills as a young boy. He was welcomed in their circle and became wise beyond his years.

Little Fawn blossomed into a beautiful young woman. Because she was a quiet girl and known to speak carefully, she often came across as mysterious, which only made her more attractive. Her long jet-black hair hung in two wide braids below her waist, and her eyes were deep velvet brown, always filled with curiosity. She was slender and small-boned, which made her appear almost fairy-like. She adored Young Eagle, her friend and constant companion.

The year that Big Buck turned twenty-seven, the death of his father, Chief Eagle Feather, made him chief of the tribe. Big Buck had never married, and he now showed signs of wanting to pursue Little Fawn. Little Fawn disliked him and avoided him as much as she could. Big Buck was bossy and cruel to anyone who dared to question his orders. He was not a gentle wise leader like his father had been, but more like a dictator who took no guidance from the elders or the spiritual healers. He was not respected by the men and most of the women feared him.

Little Fawn loved Young Eagle and had envisioned becoming his wife for as long as she could remember. Every time Big Buck approached her, she trembled and avoided looking at him directly. No matter how many times or how many ways Big Buck made advances toward her, she showed her open disdain of him. This irritated Big Buck immensely, so he grew more and more envious of Young Eagle. Everyone in the tribe assumed Young Eagle and Little Fawn would marry and have beautiful children, but Big Buck was determined never to let that happen.

If Young Eagle were out of the picture, Little Fawn would surely turn to me for help and attention, Big Buck thought. *I could give her everything, and she would realize this if Young Eagle, my only rival, were not around.* He plotted various ways to get rid of the one person who stood between him and the beautiful Little Fawn.

As summer passed, Big Buck's jealousy of Young Eagle grew stronger. The other young men in the tribe admired Young Eagle and the older men invited him to sit with them in the sweat lodge. Big Buck became even bitterer, and it showed in his attitude and behavior. The entire tribe began to question his mental stability. He was their chief, but he had no true followers. Every member of the tribe tiptoed around him from fear they might become the recipient of his unbridled anger. He blamed Young Eagle for everyone disliking him, and he was consumed by thoughts of how to get rid of him.

Throughout the summer, the tribal people had an ominous feeling. When it came time to move to their winter grounds, they grew restless waiting to hear the order from Big Buck to break camp. They waited and waited, becoming more anxious as the days passed. Big Buck ignored their pleas and obsessed continuously about how he could remove Young Eagle from the tribe. He put off the migration till weeks after they usually began their journey.

Finally, when the smell of snow was in the air and the clouds became lower and darker, Big Buck could not delay any longer and gave orders to pack up. He now had a plan to get rid of Young Eagle. After a half day's travel, the tribe stopped at the other side of the lake near the Big Spring. Each year on their final night in this area, they held a celebration feast to thank the Great Spirit and ask for a safe journey.

The women and children began the preparations for the feast while a few of the younger men, Young Eagle included, gathered their gear to hunt for fresh game. Big Buck grabbed Young Eagle's arm and said, "You hunt with me!" Young Eagle gave a single nod in agreement. The pair slipped quietly into the woods, each carrying a bow and arrows over his shoulder. When they got to the edge of the Big Spring water, Big Buck stopped and glared at Young Eagle. "I will take Little Fawn for my wife," he said. "You must leave and find a new tribe. You are no longer welcome here."

Young Eagle looked into the angry face of Big Buck and told him he would never leave Little Fawn. Big Buck became even more enraged that his order was challenged. He shoved Young Eagle as hard as he could, and Young Eagle fell to the ground. As he tried to stand up, Big Buck's leg came out to kick him, but his opponent was quick and grabbed his foot, toppling him onto the ground as well. The two scrambled to gain control of each other, yet their strength was equally matched. They were wrestling and rolling amid the fallen trees when Big Buck took out his knife and jabbed it into Young Eagle's side. Young Eagle let out a frightening scream and suddenly went limp.

Young Eagle lay there looking up with a blank stare. Big Buck rose to his feet and stood looking down at the still body, horrified at what he had done. He knelt down, felt the chest of the fallen brave, and put his ear to his mouth. No heartbeat. No breath. Young Eagle was dead.

Big Buck lifted the lifeless body of Young Eagle over his shoulder and heaved him as far as he could into the spring. He watched as Young Eagle sank to the bottom among the huge fallen trees. Big Buck then walked back to the camp. Someone noticed that Young Eagle was not with him, but Big Buck explained that Young Eagle had gone on alone tracking a deer and would catch up with them later.

Little Fawn and Robin sat around the fire waiting anxiously for Young Eagle to return, but as the night grew darker, they finally retired to their teepees. Robin encouraged Little Fawn to get some rest and reassured her that Young Eagle would be back by morning. Little Fawn knew in her heart, however, something was very wrong.

The next morning, the tribe hurried to pack up and begin the long journey. There was still no sign of Young Eagle. No one challenged Big Buck's story, even though many wondered if he had something to do with Young Eagle's disappearance. The sky was growing darker, and the impending snowstorm was fast approaching. They had to move quickly and make it farther south before a heavy snowfall blocked their trail.

The tribe moved forward without Young Eagle. Little Fawn was worried, but she had no choice. She had to leave with the group. As the long hard journey progressed, Little Fawn became withdrawn and gradually more depressed. She buried her sorrow deep in her heart, fearing the worst had happened and she would never see her handsome brave again. Little Fawn was lost without her dear friend. At sunrise every morning, Robin would see her staring far off into the north sky as if Young Eagle were going to appear.

Little Fawn felt Young Eagle beckoning her, trying to help her unravel the mystery of his disappearance. She had dreams of him being wet, shivering in the cold, calling to her. With all her mind and heart, she longed to take wings and fly back into that frozen north country to search for and find her lost love.

The winter was long and bitter cold that year in their southern camp. They wondered if spring would ever come. Little Fawn yearned to return north to find Young Eagle. Each passing week she was less the young maiden everyone knew. Her face was ashen, and she became very thin and sickly looking. Robin and Little Fawn's mother, Moonbeam, watched with aching hearts as they saw Little Fawn withering away. That happy, cheerful young girl they once knew was no longer with them.

No one spoke of Young Eagle or their suspicions of what may have happened to him, but they all suspected foul play involving their chief. A heaviness encompassed the whole tribe and a deep gloom settled in their southern camp unlike years before. Everyone—young, old, male, and female—became more and more restless and uneasy. This year, their winter home was not the place they remembered it to be. No one was able to relax. Big Buck gave orders and punished anyone who hesitated in following them by ostracizing them from the group and making them live outside the camp. He continued pursuing Little Fawn and laughed at her when she ran from him. He was cruel to the women and other young men, making rude comments about how useless they all were. Everyone avoided their chief as much as possible, which only made him more ornery and demanding.

Finally came the early signs of spring. Big Buck ordered the tribe to pack up and start preparing for their trip north. He hoped that returning to Indian Lake would bring back some of the lightness and joy they all once knew, especially for Little Fawn.

The news of heading north brought a renewed excitement and bustle to the entire group. They looked forward to the warmer weather near the lake where they had all the bounties of Great Spirit: fish, game, berries, clean water, and beautiful scenery. They felt blessed and were thankful that they would soon return to their beloved summer home.

As they prepared for their departure, Big Buck's conscience began to take hold of him. He had been taught as a young boy the "Seven Grandfather Teachings." One of those was honesty in all things. He knew he would someday pay for killing Young Eagle and lying about his disappearance. For several nights, he suffered with vivid nightmares about the night of Young Eagle's demise. He pictured his body sinking to the bottom of the Big Spring and felt the stare of Young Eagle's steel-cold eyes. He lost sleep and began totally to avoid Little Fawn. Big Buck no longer tried courting her and his behavior became more erratic. Little Fawn, still heartbroken over losing Young Eagle, withdrew further within herself and spoke to no one. Her once agile, lean body had turned frail, and her eyes were sunken deep into her face.

On the night before they left their winter camp, Little Fawn was extremely restless. She sat on the bluff all night watching the last dark shadows giving way to the first faint rays of dawn. As the sun rose, her heart felt lighter for the first time in many endless months. She was eager for this journey north, knowing it would bring her back to where she last saw Young Eagle. She had come to accept there was no life in her without him. She deeply yearned to be with him, and she knew their union was meant to be. Her hope that he was still alive had long vanished, but she still somehow knew she would be with him again. They belonged together!

Little Fawn was ready to leave before anyone else was awake. Throughout the long tedious journey, she counted each step and her feet beat out the rhythm that chanted in her mind, "Nearer, nearer." The weather did not cooperate to make the trip easy; it rained continuously for more than two weeks and the trail was muddy and difficult. The marchers were chilled to the bone and the morale of the tribe seemed to be at the lowest level possible.

They finally reached the south shore of Kitch-iti-kipi, and their spirits lifted as they began setting up camp for the night. They hoped morning would bring them clear skies and sunshine to make the final trek crossing Indian Lake to their summer destination.

Tomorrow would be Little Fawn's birthday. Robin and Little Fawn sat by the fire and talked far into the night, reminiscing about past birthdays and speaking soberly about Young Eagle. At this spot where they had last seen him, they both felt his strong presence. Little Fawn told Robin that she felt confident she and Young Eagle would soon be reunited. A light was in her eyes and a peace and contentment in her face that Robin had not seen in many moons.

Robin noticed something else about Little Fawn that night as they spoke. The light of the fire cast a glowing circle around Little Fawn's head, and she looked so beautiful gazing into the dancing flames. Robin talked of the night of the big storm, the night of Little Fawn's birth, and spoke of the powerful wind that had uprooted many trees and crashed them into the Big Spring water as if they were merely twigs. To this day, those fallen trees are seen all over in the nearby woods and at the bottom of the spring preserved by nature against the hands of time. Little Fawn told Robin she wanted to go to the spring and see those giant trees to honor the night of her birth. She planned to go at first daybreak, on her birthday.

Finally, the two went to bed. Little Fawn slept more soundly than she had in months. When she woke, the sun was just rising. She made her way to the edge of the Big Spring. There on the bank was her bark canoe tied to a tree. Young Eagle had made that canoe for her long ago. She wondered how it had gotten there since all the other canoes were at the camp. She slid into the canoe and paddled slowly toward the center of the water.

That morning, a mist surrounded the Big Spring, and the utter silence of the woods was deafening. No one was up and about yet, not even the forest animals. The easy stroke of her paddle scarcely made a ripple on the glassy, mirror-like surface. Once in the center, Little Fawn rested her paddle on the side of the canoe and sat gazing into the deep clear water. Although the water was almost two hundred feet deep, the bottom could be seen perfectly. Just as Robin had described, there were the tall gigantic trees below the surface. Little Fawn had seen them before, but she had never actually looked at them as she did now. She suddenly felt such a strong connection to them.

Little Fawn was entranced by the swirling sand between the trees. Suddenly, the sand stopped and Little Fawn gasped! The angle of the sun's rays upon the water had revealed to her the perfect form of her beloved Young Eagle. Every magnificent feature of his face and body was clearly visible. She knew why she had come! Little Fawn carefully rose to her feet in the canoe. With a loud moan and outstretched hands, she dove into the icy, cold water. An overwhelming power pulled her straight down to the bottom where Young Eagle lay waiting for her.

Big Buck had slept fitfully because of his recurring nightmares about Young Eagle. He had been fighting a strong urge to visit the Big Spring all night. As soon as the sun started to rise, he headed to the spring. As he was approaching, he saw Little Fawn stand up in her canoe and heard the echo of her moan as he watched her body go gracefully into the cold water. He yelled out her name and ran to the water's edge. He saw her body sink quickly, leaving not a ripple upon the surface. Through the clear water, he saw her reach the bottom and land right next to the still body of Young Eagle. The two of them lay side by side, their smiling faces looking up at him. Even in death, Young Eagle had won and robbed him of his love, Little Fawn! Big Buck's anger grew so great that he thought he might explode.

Big Buck turned as he heard a sound at the spring's opposite edge. Rising from the water was a small white deer. It briskly shook the water from its coat, then turned and stared directly at him before it scampered off into the woods. Big Buck shuddered, remembering his father telling him that seeing a white deer meant the Great Spirit was warning you of impending doom.

Big Buck looked back at the two lovers lying at the bottom of the spring. He stood there a long time, and his heart became overwhelmingly full of bitterness and contempt. From that moment on, Big Buck vehemently expressed his hatred for all handsome young braves, and he wanted little to do with anyone or anything. He kept to himself, like a lone wolf.

One early evening before sunset, Big Buck got in his canoe and started to paddle furiously out onto the lake. Robin watched him as he paddled faster and more frantically the farther out he went. His silhouette faded as he paddled straight into the sunset until he was no longer in sight.

That was the last time anyone saw Big Buck. The tribal members were confused. He was such an avid fisherman and swimmer that no one could believe he had drowned. However, they were also relieved to be free from his hateful and unpredictable leadership. They assumed he would return eventually, but they never saw or heard from Big Buck again.

Several months passed before the tribe began to recover from all the losses of that year. Young Eagle's disappearance, Little Fawn's desperate drowning, and the unexplained departure of Big Buck were finally in the past. Life began to feel more normal.

One day, a handsome seventeen-year-old brave named Brown Bear went fishing very near the same spot where Big Buck had paddled out. He was close enough that he could still talk with others standing on the shore. Suddenly, a huge black cloud rose from the water and surrounded Brown Bear.

Huge waves developed and crashed over his canoe, throwing Brown Bear into the lake. His friends on shore heard him cry for help. They quickly swam out to him and realized the water was not that deep. When they drew nearer, Brown Bear suddenly disappeared beneath the water. They dove under, searching for him, but he was nowhere to be found.

Several days later, Brown Bear's body floated up on the shore. On each of his ankles was a small black mark. There was a lot of fearful speculation about what had happened to him. He could have waded back to shore from where his canoe overturned! No one could explain the mysterious black cloud or the black marks on his ankles.

Weeks later, three other young braves went fishing in a large canoe also just a short distance from shore. The weather was beautiful, and the lake was calm. Out of nowhere, a powerful dark cloud surrounded them and pushed all three boys into the water. They were all good swimmers, as most Natives were, and two of the braves found safety in holding on to the overturned canoe. They reached out and grabbed their friend's arm and pulled with all their might, but they could not pull him up out of the water. He was dragged under by some immensely strong force. They had to let go or be pulled under with him. He was found the next day on the nearby shore. On each of his ankles was a small black mark, just like the marks found on Brown Bear's ankles.

Once again, the tribe was distraught. Gloom and fear settled in among them as they heard about the horror that had happened once again offshore from their camp. The elders decided they had to leave the area before they lost more of their young men.

It was still very early in the fall, but they packed up and prepared for their trip south to their winter camp much earlier than usual. Since the lake was calm and the day seemed perfect for crossing, they loaded up the canoes and began crossing to the south shore of Indian Lake.

About a quarter of a mile out from shore, a black mist rose up around them. The leading canoes were caught in what seemed like a storm of black fog whirling around them, creating a strange foam in the water. Their canoes were all overturned, but somehow, they made it to the other shore. All but one canoe, that is. The one canoe missing was that of a young brave, again a handsome seventeen-year-old, who was known for his tender and caring heart. The entire tribe mourned once again for the loss of another young brave.

Later that night, on the south shore near the Big Spring, the elders held council around a huge fire and talked well into the night about these strange happenings. They decided they could no longer make this their summer home. They believed the evil spirit of Big Buck roamed these waters, randomly taking young men's lives, and no young brave would ever be safe here again.

The small tribe of Ojibwe Indians never came back to spend their summers in this beautiful area surrounding Indian Lake and the Big Spring. Instead, they found places much farther southwest where there were many other small lakes and forests.

Epilogue

According to Aunt Pearl, several drownings happened in Indian Lake during her lifetime, all young men. Only one young woman was known to have drowned in the lake, and she was in the company of a young fisherman who also drowned.

When my aunt was older and began writing about Kitch-iti-kipi, two other young men shared stories with her of nearly drowning not far from shore on Indian Lake. Both were fishing alone on a calm day when a sudden, eerie black fog surrounded them. Out of nowhere came huge waves that capsized their boats. These men did not know each other, nor were their experiences on the same day. They each managed to save themselves and lived to tell their stories to my aunt. Both expressed their fear and swore they would never fish on Indian Lake again!

Anyone who has lived around Indian Lake, as I have, knows the lake can change from calm and serene to blustering and dangerous in a matter of minutes. Squaw Mary, who told this story to my great-great-great-grandma, was adamant that the evil spirit of Big Buck lurks on the surface of Indian Lake and is responsible for the mysterious black mist and the drownings of young men.

Be warned, boaters and fishermen! Always be careful! Wear your life jackets, no matter how good a swimmer you are! Get to shore quickly if it starts to get foggy and the lake suddenly gets rough.

Most legends have both a positive and a negative side, reflecting good versus evil. This story is no exception. Aside from the evil spirit of Big Buck lurking on Indian Lake, the other side of the story is a heartwarming contrast. Rumor has it that, on rare occasions, certain visitors at the Big Spring experience something extraordinary.

On a clear sunny day, always in the early morning hours, these few "special folks" have reported that the gurgling at the bottom of the Big Spring suddenly stops, merely for seconds. In those few seconds, they have caught a quick glimpse of Little Fawn and Young Eagle lying side by side at the bottom of the clear water. It is believed that only those people with huge hearts who have a spirit open to true, lasting, deep, and faithful love are capable of seeing this vision.

Perhaps you may be one of those special visitors! If so, I hope you will tell others of your experience and add to the legend of the beautiful and mysterious Kitch-iti-kipi!

Indian Lake and Kitch-iti-kipi

On these shores of Hiawatha, nature's Eden here below
Dwelt a tribe of red skinned[3] people, in the ancient long ago.
By the Great White Spirit guided, tall, stately like the pine;
Nourished by the first creatures, bows and arrows fed them fine.
With deer skins they built their teepees,
   teepees warmed by campfires bright.
To the rhythm of the tom-toms, danced the tribe in pure delight.

They called this the place of many rivers,
   made of bark their birch canoes;
Glided softly through the shadows, this was the life they knew.
Beside the river of laughing waters, Indian braves and chieftains too,
Changing songs of joy or woe; this was the life of
   the Chippewa Indians
Who dwelt here long ago.

I give you nature at its best, where weary souls may come and rest.
Down trails unspoiled by hands of man,
   I'll lead you through a wonderland.
And here behold an eventide, and peace within one's soul abides.
Oh, man beset by toil and strife, so weary of the battle life,
Come cast a line, and catch anew
   that faith and courage we once knew.
When bathed in sunset's afterglow, Heaven's near!
We know! We know!

- Pearl Squires Olson (Great-Great-Aunt Pearl)
1897-1969

---

[3] I have chosen to reproduce this poem as my great-great-aunt originally wrote it, with the understanding that terms like "red skinned" are considered offensive today.

About the Author and Illustrator

Author Carole Hare graduated from Manistique High School and went on to earn a bachelor's degree in business education from Lake Superior State University in Sault Ste. Marie. She taught school for three years in Monrovia, Liberia, West Africa. She later received her master's degree in counseling from Northern Michigan University. Carole worked as a counselor for twenty-seven years, twenty-three of those as a school counselor and teacher in Marquette Area Public Schools. After retiring, she moved back to Manistique to live near her elder father. She currently is employed as a licensed professional counselor at the Manistique Tribal Health Center and spends much of her free time researching and learning more about her Native American ancestors. She has two successful adult sons, two amazing daughters-in-law, and five adorable grandchildren who reside in Seattle, Washington, and St. Petersburg, Florida. For more information, check out her website at www.carolehare.com or email chare@carolehare.com.

Illustrator Ryan Gilroy attended Kendall College of Art and Design. During his first year of art school, he was called into the ministry. Ryan graduated from Great Lakes Christian College where he earned his Bachelor of Religious Education. For the past twenty years, he has been a pastor. Currently, Ryan has started a church in Manistique where he also teaches art at the elementary school and lives with his wife and four children. Ryan has always loved the Upper Peninsula of Michigan. Inspired by its beauty and relaxed lifestyle, it is where he continues to create art.